W9-DIJ-346

Bears

PHOTOS AND FACTS FOR EVERYONE

BY ISIS GAILLARD

Learn With Facts Series

Book 1

Dedicated to my boys, Jaxon and Jalen

CONTENTS

Isis Gaillard. Bears: Photos and Facts for Everyone (Learn With Facts Series Book 1).
Ebook Edition.
Learn With Facts an imprint of TLM Media LLC

eISBN: 978-1-62327-755-0
ISBN-13: 978-1-62327-756-7
Hardback: 979-8-88700-449-5

Introduction

Bears are warm-blooded creatures of the family Ursidae. Bears are grouped as cuneiforms, or pooch like carnivores, with the pinnipeds being their closest living relatives.

Even though just eight types of bears are surviving, they are broad, showing up in a full mixed bag of natural surroundings all through the Northern Hemisphere and halfway in the Southern Hemisphere.

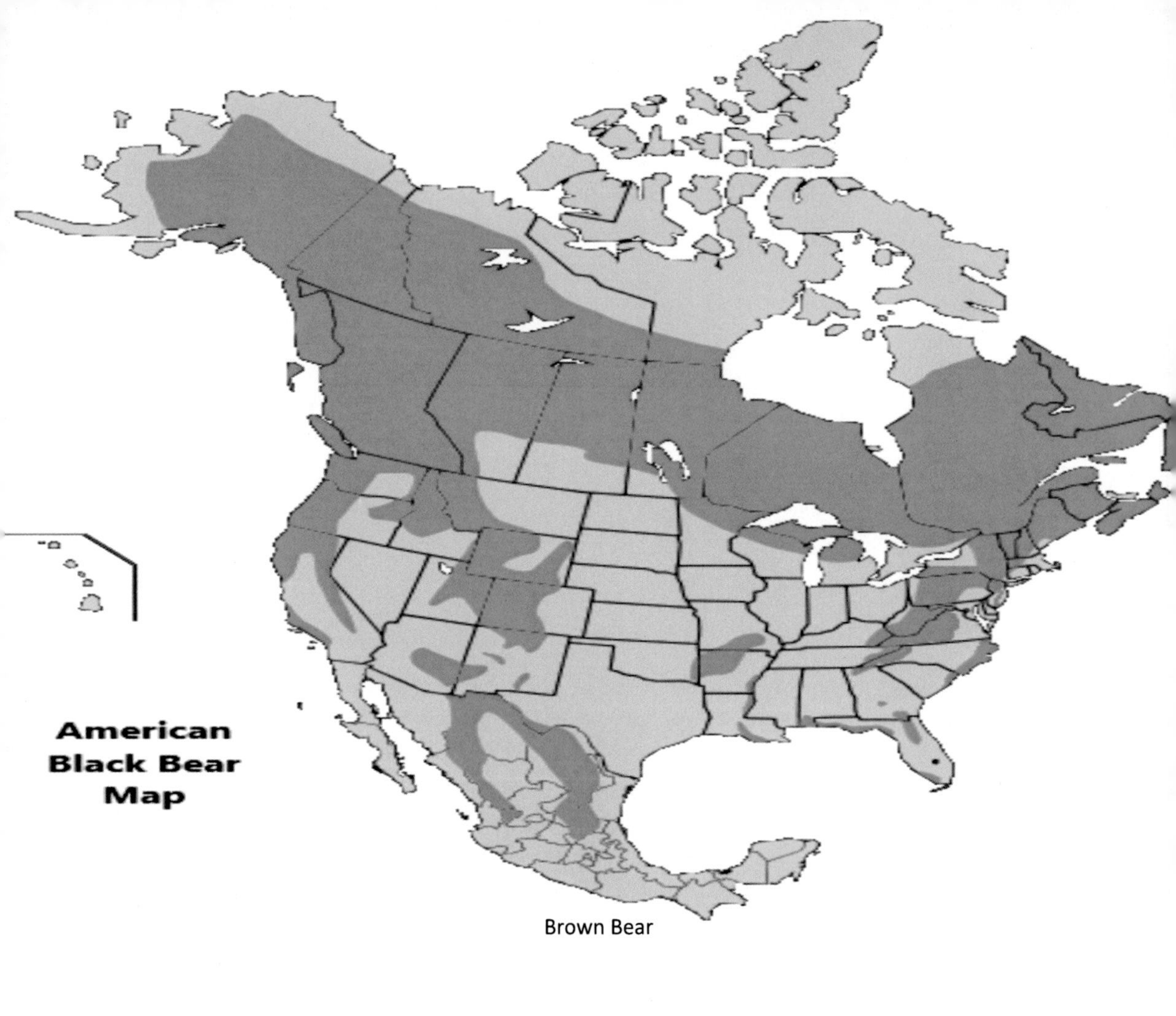

Black_bear_map.png: *Map_Black_Bear.svg: Kmusserderivative work: Bobisbob (talk)derivative work: Bobisbob / CC BY-SA (https://creativecommons.org/licenses/by-sa/3.0)

Bears are discovered on the landmasses of North America, South America, Europe, and Asia. They are ordinarily vast animals and are described by a plant grade stroll (on their heels, such as people), a towering figure, short legs, a stub of a tail, minor, adjust ears, and forward confronting eyes.

Description

here are eight living species on the planet, et here we talk over six sorts of bears.

. **Spectacled Bear** (Tremarctos ornatus): pectacled bears are the main types of bears hat exist in South America. They have been listinguished around Venezuela, Columbia, cuador, Bolivia, and Peru. Males are a third igger than females in sizes and now and gain twice their weight. The male bear veighs 100–200 kg (220–440 lb), and the emale bear weighs 35–82 kg. Length runs rom 120 to 200 cm (47–79 in), with a tail ength of 7 cm (2.8 in), and stature from 60 to 0 cm (24–30 in).

Spectacle Bear

2. **Sun Bear** (Helarctos malayanus): Sun bear is the littlest bear species on the planet. A fully developed male might tip the scales at scarcely 66-154 pounds while females are even littler, running 44-88 pounds. Sun bears have dim dark or dark tan hide with an orange-yellow horseshoe shape in the midsection normal for this species. This specific type of bear adores the hotter atmospheres.

They are discovered in the tropical rainforest territories where the temperatures are from 78 to 82 degrees.

3. **Sloth Bear** (Melursus ursinus): The sloth bear is discovered in India, Sri Lanka, Nepal, Bhutan, and Bangladesh. They might be found in the meadows or the moist locales at higher rises. The grown-up males can weigh up to 120-400 pounds, 220 pounds being an average standard, and might have a figure length of 4.6 to 6.3 ft. The females are somewhat more diminutive than males.

Sloth Bear

Asian Black Bear

4. **Asian Black Bear** (Ursus thibetanus): The Asian black bear is everything dark, with the exception of a white sickle molded range in the midsection area. The bears, as mentioned above, are discovered just in Asia in nations like Korea, China, Russia, and Japan. They are medium-measured stays the males weighing something like 200-330 pounds and the females around 143-198 pounds.

American Black Bear

5. **American Black Bear** (Ursus Americanus): The American dark discovered in North America. The span of the male bears can extend from 130 pounds to 550 pounds, while females extend from 90 to 370 pounds. The for the most part size frequently hinges on what part of America they happen to exist in, yet a large portion of them are 120 to 200 cm when they are fully developed. This implies that they can arrive at up to 6.4 feet in stature when they stand upright.

6. **Tan Bear** (Ursus arctos): The brown bear is the most extensively appropriated of all bears. Subspecies might be discovered in the different areas of Asia, North America, and Europe, Russia, Canada, and colder parts of the United States. They have an average size of about 5.6 to 9.2 feet tall for fully developed males.

dditionally, there is a significant contrast in the
eight of the grown-ups, however. While the
ales for the littlest subspecies like the Eurasian
rown bear might be 200 pounds, the biggest
ubspecies like the Kodiak bear might be, on
verage, 1500 pounds with a heaviest recorded
eigh in the vicinity of 2,500 pounds. Females
re about 30% less of those measurements.

Tan Bear

Size

Even though bears have comparable shapes, they come in altogether different sizes. The biggest bear of all is the Kodiak, an Alaskan tan bear. Other colossal tan bears, for example, the grizzly, rank third regarding the size.

Kodiak Bear

Particular bears are honestly short in size. Spectacled bears, American dark bears, sloth bears, and Asian dark bears are everything about the same length. Spectacled bears weigh more than the other three types of bears, on the other hand. Sloth bears weigh less than the other three. The most modest of every last one of bears are the sun bears. Inside every assembly of bears, certain parts are more significant than others. Males in a gathering are ordinarily greater than females.

Sloth Bear

Most tan bears and American dark bears have tan or dark hide. Sun bears, sloth bears, and Asiatic dark bears regularly have a white or yellow-white fix on their midsection. Spectacled bears have white or yellow-white loops around their eyes. This makes them appear as if they are wearing eyeglasses or "exhibitions."

The bear has an enormous head; short, erect ears; and short, compelling appendages. Its teeth are utilized for both grinding and tearing. Bears have an underprivileged vision and listening to, however, a sharp feeling of odor. Every foot has five long, sharp, bent hooks utilized for climbing, burrowing, and holding prey. The bear moves with a blundering, even footed stride yet can run quickly when indispensable. Bears can run up to 35 miles (56 km) for every hour for short removes. They often stand and stroll on their rear legs, utilizing their forepaws to arrive at heightened questions. Bears are apt tree climbers and

Two Bears Climbing a tree

Old Brown Bear

Bears usually exist from 15 to 25 years in the wild and up to 45 years in imprisonment. Most species are lethargic throughout the winter, dozing in hollows, sanctums dug in the earth, or other ensured places.

Offspring are born in the spring; one set is an ordinary litter. Offspring are extremely modest at conception, weighing from 8 to 16 ounces (230 to 450 grams). They stay with their mother for more than a year.

Breeding

The age at which bears arrive at sexual development is exceedingly variable, both between and inside species. Sexual development is reliant on form condition, which is, in turn, subordinate upon the nourishment supply ready to the single developing person. The females of more modest species might have a junior in as meager as two years, though the more prominent species may not raise youthful until they are four or even nine years of age. Initially, rearing maybe even later in males, where rivalry for mates might leave more youthful males without access to females.

Bear With Bear Cubs

‾he bear's dating period is extremely short. 3ears in northern atmospheres replicate ;easonally, generally after a time of dormancy :omparable to hibernation, granted that ropical species breed lasting through the year.)ffspring are born toothless, blind, and bare. ‾he fledglings of tan bears, typically born in itters of one to three, will ordinarily stay with he mother for two full flavors.

Two Bears Breeding

Bear Cubs Playing

They eat their mother's drain through the term of their association with their mother, in spite of the fact that as the whelps press on to develop, nurturing comes to be less continuous and whelps figure out how to start chasing with the mother. They will stay with the mother in the ballpark of three years until she drops in the following cycle of estrus and drives the fledglings off.

Bear Mother and her Cubs

Bears will arrive at sexual development in five to seven years. Male bears, in particular polar and tan bears, will kill; and some of the time devours whelps destined to another father to incite a female to breed once more. Female bears are regularly efficacious in driving off males in insurance of their offspring, despite being quite more diminutive.

Eating Habit

Bears eat fish, well-evolved creatures, apples and oranges, roots, seeds, creepy crawlies, flesh, and nectar. The point when a bear discovers a home of wild honeybees, it tears the home separated and devours the nectar. The animal's thick hide ensures it from bumblebee stings; the main unprotected spot is the nose.

Bear catching fish for food

Interesting Facts

While numerous individuals think bears are nocturnal, they are usually diurnal, dynamic for the most part throughout the day. The conviction that they are nocturnal clearly originates from the propensities of bears that exist close to people, which participate in some nighttime exercises, for example, attacking junk jars or crops while dodging people.

Sloth Bear sitting on a rock

The sloth bear of Asia is the most nocturnal of the bears, yet these shifts by single, and females with whelps are regularly diurnal to escape rivalry with males and nighttime predators. Bears are overwhelmingly singular and are recognized to be the most asocial of the entire Carnivore.

Contacts between rearing bears are short, and the primary time bears experienced in modest gatherings are mothers with junior or infrequent seasonal bounties of rich nourishment. Bears can see and catch like us. Bears have an extremely exceptional feeling of odor. Bears can stand on their rear legs to smell and see better. Bears are savvy and curious animals. Numerous bears live where the winter is exceptionally icy.

Bear in Winter

In the spots mentioned above, bears will find or make a cave. They will drop in the lair when it gets too chilly and stays there until spring. This profound slumber is called "hibernation." Bears won't consume or drink throughout this time. Whelps are born while the mother bear is sleeping.

THE END

Thanks for reading facts about Bears. I am a parent of two boys on the autism spectrum. I am always advocating for Autism Spectrum Disorders which part of the proceeds of this book goes to many Non-Profit Autism Organizations. I would love if you would leave a review.

Author Note from Isis Gaillard:

Thanks For Reading! I hope you enjoyed the fact book about Bears.

Please check out all the Learn With Facts and the Kids Learn With Pictures series available.

Visit www.IsisGaillard.com and www.LearnWithFacts.com to find more books in the Learn With Facts Series

More Books In The Series

Over 75 books in the Learn With Facts Series.

Word Search 1

T	Z	V	A	P	O	F	R	V	I
S	U	L	A	S	M	V	L	Q	E
E	B	K	D	Z	E	C	O	B	N
L	C	R	B	I	G	R	E	S	T
B	I	O	V	F	T	A	X	V	Z
B	E	J	Y	L	V	Q	F	P	O
U	J	A	I	E	L	V	R	I	T
Z	K	U	R	M	H	Q	E	Z	J
S	M	S	I	S	N	F	K	W	L
V	P	Z	S	W	G	H	M	K	M

Word List

Bears
Beavers
Birds

Word Search 2

C	R	T	Q	I	K	B	J	S	G
H	E	Z	A	U	W	G	N	R	A
A	X	L	G	M	X	I	Z	J	J
M	U	N	E	P	H	P	B	G	P
E	I	J	L	P	K	T	F	B	M
L	Z	Z	L	E	H	E	O	E	Q
E	J	O	X	U	U	A	I	F	L
O	D	X	G	N	B	Y	N	J	Z
N	P	Q	D	S	I	P	C	T	P
S	O	C	B	C	S	M	W	E	S

Word List

Elephants
Dolphins
Chameleons

Word Search 3

W	C	F	F	A	F	H	O	R	C
L	R	D	C	D	X	U	P	S	H
S	O	I	F	Z	H	M	H	S	E
M	C	X	J	D	T	F	R	C	E
S	O	U	M	U	O	A	F	C	T
K	D	B	F	O	G	L	Z	H	A
Y	I	R	S	U	U	V	Y	M	H
J	L	H	O	A	V	D	J	D	S
R	E	C	D	K	T	K	Q	R	K
F	S	L	J	M	C	O	J	K	O

Word List

Cheetahs
Cougars
Crocodiles

Word Search 4

Y	J	C	Q	Q	C	I	X	Y	Z
N	V	A	K	S	F	Y	K	O	S
O	G	D	L	G	O	Z	P	R	R
O	W	T	Z	G	X	C	U	S	X
Y	K	W	D	N	E	A	Z	E	N
C	K	W	Z	U	S	M	H	L	U
D	N	C	V	O	J	K	L	G	P
P	P	R	N	X	W	Y	G	A	G
D	K	I	J	L	O	H	H	E	P
Q	D	F	L	M	K	T	B	B	Z

Word List

Dinosaurs
Eagles
Foxes

Word Search 5

P	S	F	F	R	N	C	Q	R	H
Z	D	N	T	B	W	J	E	Z	E
G	U	Z	E	T	Q	S	B	G	D
A	B	J	F	G	K	G	M	I	G
A	V	M	L	S	G	O	W	R	E
Q	C	G	M	M	C	R	C	A	H
C	I	D	S	S	Z	F	P	F	O
A	I	K	L	L	J	L	W	F	G
M	C	S	B	H	M	A	B	E	S
U	P	F	T	W	T	D	I	S	G

Word List

Frogs
Giraffes
Hedgehogs

Word Search 6

K	F	K	S	K	F	W	Z	R	S
Z	A	V	K	P	S	O	O	E	A
J	K	N	Y	Q	M	L	S	H	Z
U	O	U	G	W	P	R	O	V	X
U	A	N	R	A	O	J	S	W	I
I	L	C	S	H	R	I	D	Y	B
T	A	Q	L	N	F	O	N	W	K
L	S	N	R	D	O	H	O	T	W
S	D	Y	Z	W	L	I	G	S	D
D	D	R	P	T	A	Z	L	O	C

Word List

Horses
Kangaroos
Koalas
Lions

Word Search 7

S	H	P	L	U	S	D	L	S	A
L	Q	N	N	S	P	P	P	K	U
W	P	J	X	N	L	K	J	C	S
O	A	H	X	I	L	V	X	O	L
W	N	E	Y	U	W	R	Y	C	D
U	D	G	G	G	C	N	N	A	G
J	A	L	S	N	L	D	T	E	E
P	S	O	E	E	S	W	H	P	Z
U	Z	U	X	P	V	C	L	L	Q
E	L	F	Z	L	Q	F	P	K	P

Word List

Owls
Pandas
Peacocks
Penguins

Word Search 8

R	H	I	N	O	C	E	R	O	S
Y	T	I	A	W	W	Z	U	Z	E
W	Y	S	S	E	V	S	V	D	A
F	M	S	R	S	Q	C	Q	N	T
W	B	N	R	E	G	L	D	Z	U
R	W	A	Y	K	D	H	V	S	R
S	O	K	B	J	Q	I	G	U	T
L	E	E	C	C	B	H	P	P	L
V	Y	S	B	R	E	F	V	S	E
X	A	G	C	A	H	M	N	J	S

Word List

Rhinoceros
SeaTurtles
Snakes
Spiders

Word Search 9

B	Y	A	V	N	A	D	N	Z	M
U	F	L	T	K	W	Z	Y	F	S
F	X	P	W	I	A	T	M	D	A
T	K	A	J	S	G	Y	Z	F	R
J	J	C	K	G	Z	E	V	R	B
U	I	A	Q	X	C	Y	R	K	E
O	J	S	A	N	T	K	G	S	Z
I	S	S	J	R	T	N	P	M	A
D	Z	E	R	J	S	B	X	H	P
A	L	L	I	G	A	T	O	R	S

Word List

Tigers
Zebras
Alpacas
Alligators

Word Search 10

U	L	H	H	A	X	E	V	T	L
P	A	P	B	S	Z	P	H	B	S
G	S	Y	V	Y	G	Q	W	U	E
T	C	O	D	Q	D	O	E	I	P
Q	B	T	V	S	E	E	Y	S	W
M	C	F	H	P	M	A	V	L	E
E	W	M	M	A	A	S	U	E	H
F	D	O	O	Z	B	Z	O	M	Z
O	T	W	H	S	N	U	B	A	D
L	A	E	A	H	Y	K	A	C	A

Word List

Camels

Word Search 11

E	Q	I	Z	M	V	O	D	Q	C
K	O	Y	Q	G	U	H	Z	H	R
E	I	G	S	D	S	A	K	U	F
U	G	E	N	I	N	I	Z	B	I
Z	E	K	F	I	L	J	V	A	U
B	Q	F	P	H	M	T	G	T	E
L	W	J	F	I	G	A	A	S	V
L	Z	O	R	F	S	Z	L	F	A
M	K	P	P	F	B	O	M	F	Y
Z	F	K	X	A	S	O	J	O	Q

Word List

Bees
Bats
Fish
Flamingo

Word Search 12

A	D	G	A	Z	E	L	L	E	I
T	S	T	W	Q	P	E	H	Q	G
C	T	T	E	W	Q	C	T	P	U
O	R	Y	C	U	N	T	I	X	A
U	A	T	Z	E	U	L	L	X	N
H	N	Q	Z	E	S	M	U	C	A
P	U	M	P	R	P	N	B	F	S
P	K	H	Y	E	N	A	I	G	B
B	Y	Y	T	Q	D	M	Q	G	F
M	X	U	B	Q	W	P	Y	U	C

Word List

Gazelle
Hyena
Iguanas
Insects

Word Search 13

H	S	I	F	Y	L	L	E	J	A
M	S	F	M	T	R	I	H	I	L
P	S	D	S	W	Z	B	E	J	N
Z	R	Z	R	W	U	B	G	Y	F
R	A	Q	V	A	X	G	D	D	M
O	U	Z	C	K	P	A	Y	D	Q
M	G	W	M	A	A	O	A	L	U
P	A	Y	J	P	W	G	E	S	Y
U	J	H	I	S	I	J	Z	L	B
O	Q	H	A	I	H	L	R	Z	C

Word List

Jaguars
Jellyfish
Leopards

Word Search 14

R	F	Y	Q	F	Z	K	G	Z	M
K	A	Z	O	M	Y	J	M	P	O
R	N	Z	F	I	S	E	P	E	O
D	V	R	K	P	E	J	K	S	S
D	P	D	Y	R	J	T	D	C	E
E	J	W	K	G	X	R	B	L	L
V	I	A	T	Q	A	A	Y	J	P
D	T	N	Z	Z	W	N	D	K	F
S	J	A	I	F	X	H	D	K	Y
P	F	L	G	R	O	I	A	G	J

Word List

Lizards
Lynx
Meerkat
Moose

Word Search 15

Y	F	O	L	K	X	O	K	O	S
H	M	Z	G	G	X	S	C	F	T
Q	S	A	V	T	M	T	Z	C	V
X	V	S	N	O	O	R	P	Y	Q
F	X	X	M	P	S	I	A	L	I
E	K	M	U	H	K	C	R	V	J
Z	M	S	F	E	B	H	R	X	D
O	E	Z	V	C	J	E	O	V	K
S	R	Y	I	F	X	S	T	Z	S
O	F	A	K	H	R	V	S	C	L

Word List

Octopuses
Ostriches
Parrots

Word Search 16

O	M	N	G	J	F	W	S	D	K
G	Y	I	V	U	T	S	R	F	R
P	C	H	J	T	G	M	A	P	J
P	O	Z	M	E	U	R	E	J	V
Z	O	N	X	O	K	L	B	F	V
X	V	N	I	B	I	T	R	Q	G
H	X	P	I	C	F	R	A	E	I
R	L	S	A	E	T	Q	L	S	S
J	Y	N	N	S	S	E	O	E	W
L	S	K	D	X	B	V	P	L	P

Word List

Pelicans
Polar Bears
Ponies

Word Search 17

S	C	O	R	P	I	O	N	S	T
I	J	S	Q	X	V	P	E	T	L
X	X	L	R	W	K	S	K	R	K
L	H	O	V	E	R	Z	B	O	L
Y	O	Q	X	O	T	S	Y	Q	V
E	M	H	H	J	U	S	Z	M	T
J	Q	A	T	U	B	C	O	I	C
G	E	A	H	Q	D	N	J	O	E
S	O	C	A	Y	H	V	S	T	R
K	Y	G	O	I	D	X	Z	L	P

Word List

Roosters
Scorpions
Seahorses

Word Search 18

J	J	S	G	U	T	T	H	F	W
S	P	E	O	N	R	D	T	S	H
S	M	L	Z	Q	P	I	P	A	S
D	Z	T	U	Y	P	I	D	X	I
W	D	R	A	R	X	W	T	A	F
Z	V	U	I	N	D	Z	N	P	R
M	X	T	C	A	V	Y	U	R	A
X	W	Q	S	W	A	N	S	I	T
V	Z	B	H	P	S	G	X	L	S
X	X	X	C	W	U	K	G	C	K

Word List

Starfish
Swans
Turtles

Word Search 19

P	Z	Y	X	A	X	D	H	X	V
F	H	A	N	T	E	A	T	E	R
M	D	Z	T	L	U	C	B	C	S
A	R	M	A	D	I	L	L	O	E
A	D	D	E	H	D	D	Y	S	L
B	V	K	E	T	U	Q	D	E	A
U	Y	U	Q	X	H	R	D	V	H
N	G	Q	X	H	I	H	G	L	W
Q	G	W	V	I	Q	M	T	O	K
Q	D	Z	C	I	G	Z	D	W	M

Word List

Whales
Wolves
Anteater
Armadillo

Word Search 20

P	V	I	C	C	W	E	R	T	S
J	C	H	I	P	M	U	N	K	S
S	J	O	L	A	F	F	U	B	Z
S	N	B	E	H	A	O	J	S	N
U	E	E	P	H	J	H	V	A	R
W	E	F	K	A	S	E	B	E	B
K	N	Y	J	C	C	O	W	S	G
P	P	D	O	C	I	S	E	O	A
E	X	H	A	Y	W	H	L	S	G
N	W	J	R	P	H	P	C	Q	V

Word List

Buffalo
Chickens
Chipmunks
Cows

Word Search 21

O	U	I	A	U	Y	D	R	V	A
B	Q	P	M	C	B	V	I	V	A
X	L	E	A	N	D	I	H	C	E
O	I	K	D	V	K	K	P	Z	D
V	S	R	T	V	X	V	N	R	S
D	O	N	K	E	Y	S	K	F	J
T	D	M	E	U	G	F	J	V	Q
L	C	E	A	K	J	W	S	A	F
Z	M	H	E	J	M	Q	W	M	F
G	I	P	J	R	M	K	I	Q	M

Word List

Deer
Donkeys
Echidna
Emu

Word Search 22

X	E	B	Q	S	X	O	D	P	S
H	G	O	A	T	S	U	R	G	X
S	B	L	N	A	W	X	I	S	U
R	F	M	V	I	T	P	G	D	O
L	H	J	C	W	A	Q	C	I	I
L	O	S	T	E	R	R	E	F	C
A	D	A	N	S	Y	V	H	C	J
M	B	I	K	P	C	V	Q	K	H
A	U	K	Z	N	X	S	H	E	W
G	S	F	B	L	Q	J	C	E	Y

Word List

Ferrets
Goats
Guinea Pigs
Llama

Word Search 23

I	P	L	A	T	Y	P	U	S	P
S	Q	F	H	S	K	Z	A	S	T
H	M	R	Y	A	L	H	V	N	V
S	J	U	A	C	V	D	W	O	W
S	E	N	I	P	U	C	R	O	P
S	V	N	B	S	K	G	Y	C	D
U	M	N	P	L	H	L	I	C	G
W	D	L	C	Q	X	J	R	A	N
C	G	N	M	N	D	W	N	R	I
E	N	U	P	H	Q	R	Y	I	S

Word List

Platypus
Porcupines
Raccoons

Word Search 24

Y	W	A	X	M	L	T	Z	I	R
E	N	R	L	T	T	Z	T	N	X
X	D	B	E	E	P	T	D	H	O
Y	S	R	S	E	U	N	P	P	D
D	L	K	E	H	D	A	K	G	V
N	H	H	U	H	A	N	F	D	C
M	S	I	D	N	K	R	I	C	V
X	L	Y	C	X	K	P	K	E	B
N	Q	U	W	N	D	S	Q	S	R
Y	M	C	T	G	M	G	D	E	R

Word List

Reindeer
Sharks
Sheep
Skunks

Word Search 25

C	L	V	M	B	B	O	I	P	F
K	V	M	C	N	A	L	O	P	S
M	S	S	L	V	V	F	U	Q	S
R	M	K	J	F	Y	B	U	H	T
Y	M	R	B	I	X	I	T	L	I
V	V	O	A	X	R	O	X	X	I
V	S	T	O	R	L	Z	L	W	N
M	N	S	E	S	K	W	V	Z	F
R	A	L	O	B	J	N	Q	K	E
M	S	K	K	N	J	H	R	E	G

Word List

Sloths
Squirrels
Storks

Word Search 26

U	W	I	K	C	O	S	E	S	J
I	V	W	J	Z	L	T	S	F	M
Z	M	N	A	A	G	U	O	P	M
T	B	J	M	D	R	R	Z	V	O
U	A	M	E	L	Q	K	K	D	S
X	A	F	A	L	B	E	I	K	T
M	F	W	N	F	A	Y	A	H	X
L	V	T	Y	D	X	Y	G	H	X
F	F	E	M	F	S	M	S	J	A
Z	I	J	Y	A	C	I	N	O	U

Word List

Turkey
Walrus
Yaks
Mammals

Word Search 27

T	A	B	G	U	V	S	F	R	I
T	N	N	N	M	I	K	O	N	J
N	C	A	T	T	L	E	Q	W	X
J	M	X	F	E	A	S	G	B	M
U	Y	O	C	D	L	C	Q	L	N
H	K	O	D	P	D	O	R	Y	L
U	B	B	L	D	K	M	P	P	U
S	S	E	T	O	Y	O	C	E	E
S	K	R	A	V	D	R	A	A	S
E	V	N	T	K	D	S	Q	I	M

Word List

Aardvarks
Antelopes
Cattle
Coyotes

Word Search 28

X	P	G	L	X	A	H	W	P	G
K	A	O	Q	E	Y	Z	R	S	O
A	N	Z	G	Y	M	M	M	G	R
A	T	U	W	I	M	U	M	F	I
C	H	V	T	C	S	Z	R	R	L
R	E	E	K	S	F	S	S	S	L
W	R	M	O	B	V	M	D	V	A
G	S	P	M	I	O	K	V	Q	S
S	O	H	A	W	G	I	O	P	R
Q	I	Z	P	F	X	H	E	T	C

Word List

Gorillas
Lemurs
Opossums
Panthers

Word Search 29

Y	V	A	V	W	G	B	J	D	W
T	Z	K	O	B	O	J	C	F	P
G	W	N	V	U	Y	U	W	U	W
V	R	F	I	O	N	Z	F	M	E
D	C	I	B	F	X	F	P	L	A
M	W	Q	X	W	I	N	X	F	S
Z	X	X	E	N	R	Z	D	W	E
C	O	O	S	Q	Q	B	G	T	L
S	E	S	I	O	T	R	O	T	S
H	C	U	V	I	N	S	D	E	E

Word List

Puffins
Tortoises
Weasels

Word Search 30

M	P	L	A	F	X	H	E	H	D
S	F	Y	M	E	X	W	B	U	M
E	M	H	P	W	C	S	V	F	P
N	K	M	H	F	Z	A	R	L	P
U	J	C	I	O	S	L	A	H	Q
T	M	Q	B	R	J	Q	F	F	E
I	H	E	I	B	B	X	V	I	P
X	A	E	A	F	Q	L	Q	E	Q
I	F	A	N	F	T	T	N	Y	F
A	Z	H	S	J	O	S	U	Y	D

Word List

Amphibians

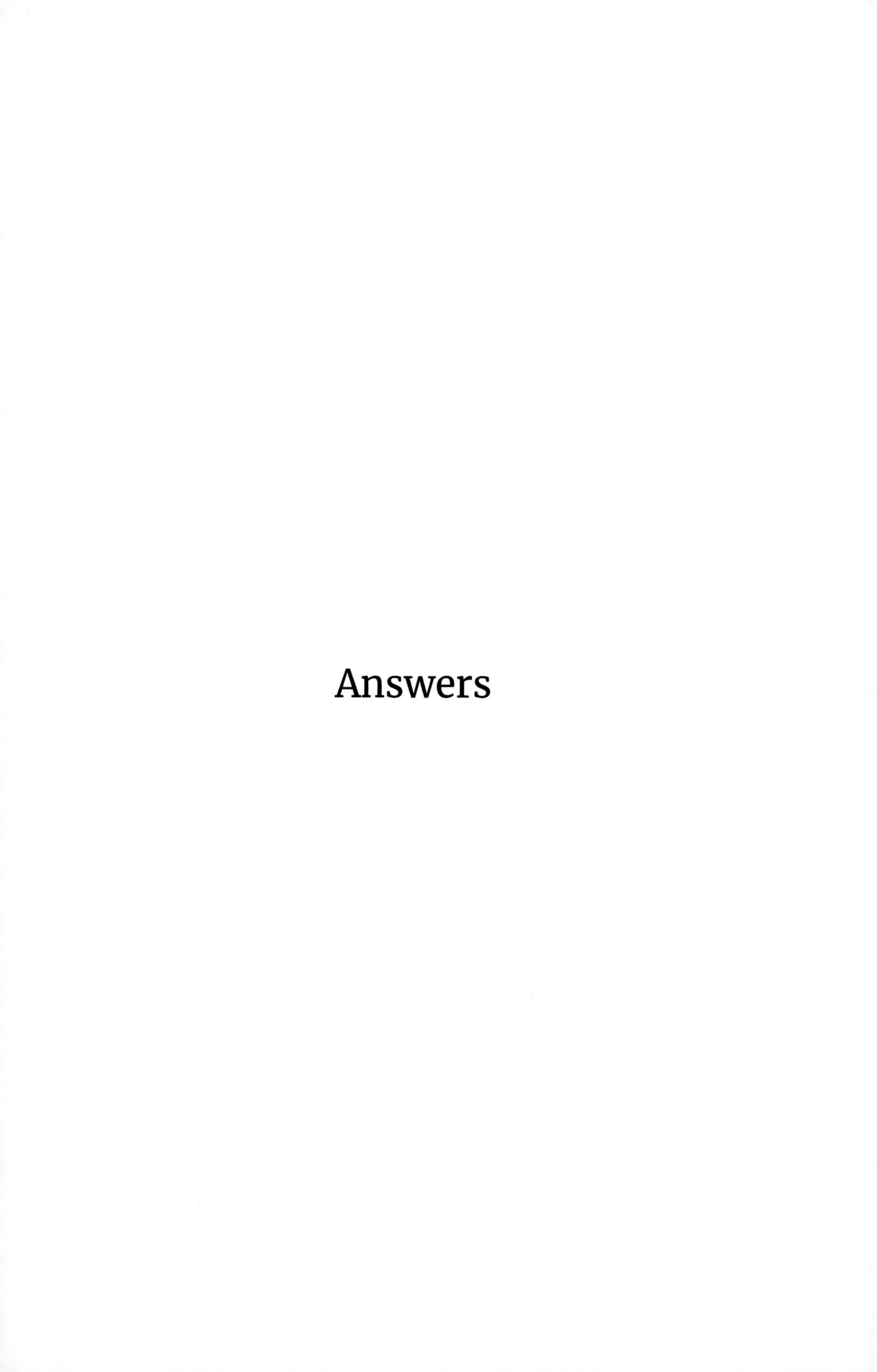

Answers

Word Search 1

T	Z	V	A	P	O	F	R	V	I
S	U	L	A	S	M	V	L	Q	E
E	B	K	D	Z	E	C	O	B	N
L	C	R	B	I	G	R	E	S	T
B	I	O	V	F	T	A	X	V	Z
B	E	J	Y	L	V	Q	F	P	O
U	J	A	I	E	L	V	R	I	T
Z	K	U	R	M	H	Q	E	Z	J
S	M	S	I	S	N	F	K	W	L
V	P	Z	S	W	G	H	M	K	M

Word Search 2

C	R	T	Q	I	K	B	J	S	G
H	E	Z	A	U	W	G	N	R	A
A	X	L	G	M	X	I	Z	J	J
M	U	N	E	P	H	P	B	G	P
E	I	J	L	P	K	T	F	B	M
L	Z	Z	L	E	H	E	O	E	Q
E	J	O	X	U	U	A	I	F	L
O	D	X	G	N	B	Y	N	J	Z
N	P	Q	D	S	I	P	C	T	P
S	O	C	B	C	S	M	W	E	S

Word Search 3

W	C	F	F	A	F	H	O	R	C
L	R	D	C	D	X	U	P	S	H
S	O	I	F	Z	H	M	H	S	E
M	C	X	J	D	T	F	R	C	E
S	O	U	M	U	O	A	F	C	T
K	D	B	F	O	G	L	Z	H	A
Y	I	R	S	U	U	V	Y	M	H
J	L	H	O	A	V	D	J	D	S
R	E	C	D	K	T	K	Q	R	K
F	S	L	J	M	C	O	J	K	O

Word Search 4

Y	J	C	Q	Q	C	I	X	Y	Z
N	V	A	K	S	F	Y	K	O	S
O	G	D	L	G	O	Z	P	R	R
O	W	T	Z	G	X	C	U	S	X
Y	K	W	D	N	E	A	Z	E	N
C	K	W	Z	U	S	M	H	L	U
D	N	C	V	O	J	K	L	G	P
P	P	R	N	X	W	Y	G	A	G
D	K	I	J	L	O	H	H	E	P
Q	D	F	L	M	K	T	B	B	Z

Word Search 5

P	S	F	F	R	N	C	Q	R	H
Z	D	N	T	B	W	J	E	Z	E
G	U	Z	E	T	Q	S	B	G	D
A	B	J	F	G	K	G	M	I	G
A	V	M	L	S	G	O	W	R	E
Q	C	G	M	M	C	R	C	A	H
C	I	D	S	S	Z	F	P	F	O
A	I	K	L	L	J	L	W	F	G
M	C	S	B	H	M	A	B	E	S
U	P	F	T	W	T	D	I	S	G

Word Search 6

K	F	K	S	K	F	W	Z	R	S
Z	A	V	K	P	S	O	O	E	A
J	K	N	Y	Q	M	L	S	H	Z
U	O	U	G	W	P	R	O	V	X
U	A	N	R	A	O	J	S	W	I
I	L	C	S	H	R	I	D	Y	B
T	A	Q	L	N	F	O	N	W	K
L	S	N	R	D	O	H	O	T	W
S	D	Y	Z	W	L	I	G	S	D
D	D	R	P	T	A	Z	L	O	C

Word Search 7

S	H	P	L	U	S	D	L	S	A
L	Q	N	N	S	P	P	P	K	U
W	P	J	X	N	L	K	J	C	S
O	A	H	X	I	L	V	X	O	L
W	N	E	Y	U	W	R	Y	C	D
U	D	G	G	G	C	N	N	A	G
J	A	L	S	N	L	D	T	E	E
P	S	O	E	E	S	W	H	P	Z
U	Z	U	X	P	V	C	L	L	Q
E	L	F	Z	L	Q	F	P	K	P

Word Search 8

R	H	I	N	O	C	E	R	O	S
Y	T	I	A	W	W	Z	U	Z	E
W	Y	S	S	E	V	S	V	D	A
F	M	S	R	S	Q	C	Q	N	T
W	B	N	R	E	G	L	D	Z	U
R	W	A	Y	K	D	H	V	S	R
S	O	K	B	J	Q	I	G	U	T
L	E	E	C	C	B	H	P	P	L
V	Y	S	B	R	E	F	V	S	E
X	A	G	C	A	H	M	N	J	S

Word Search 9

B	Y	A	V	N	A	D	N	Z	M
U	F	L	T	K	W	Z	Y	F	S
F	X	P	W	I	A	T	M	D	A
T	K	A	J	S	G	Y	Z	F	R
J	J	C	K	G	Z	E	V	R	B
U	I	A	Q	X	C	Y	R	K	E
O	J	S	A	N	T	K	G	S	Z
I	S	S	J	R	T	N	P	M	A
D	Z	E	R	J	S	B	X	H	P
A	L	L	I	G	A	T	O	R	S

Word Search 10

U	L	H	H	A	X	E	V	T	L
P	A	P	B	S	Z	P	H	B	S
G	S	Y	V	Y	G	Q	W	U	E
T	C	O	D	Q	D	O	E	I	P
Q	B	T	V	S	E	E	Y	S	W
M	C	F	H	P	M	A	V	L	E
E	W	M	M	A	A	S	U	E	H
F	D	O	O	Z	B	Z	O	M	Z
O	T	W	H	S	N	U	B	A	D
L	A	E	A	H	Y	K	A	C	A

Word Search 11

E	Q	I	Z	M	V	O	D	Q	C
K	O	Y	Q	G	U	H	Z	H	R
E	I	G	S	D	S	A	K	U	F
U	G	E	N	I	N	I	Z	B	I
Z	E	K	F	I	L	J	V	A	U
B	Q	F	P	H	M	T	G	T	E
L	W	J	F	I	G	A	A	S	V
L	Z	O	R	F	S	Z	L	F	A
M	K	P	P	F	B	O	M	F	Y
Z	F	K	X	A	S	O	J	O	Q

Word Search 12

A	D	G	A	Z	E	L	L	E	I
T	S	T	W	Q	P	E	H	Q	G
C	T	T	E	W	Q	C	T	P	U
O	R	Y	C	U	N	T	I	X	A
U	A	T	Z	E	U	L	L	X	N
H	N	Q	Z	E	S	M	U	C	A
P	U	M	P	R	P	N	B	F	S
P	K	H	Y	E	N	A	I	G	B
B	Y	Y	T	Q	D	M	Q	G	F
M	X	U	B	Q	W	P	Y	U	C

Word Search 13

H	S	I	F	Y	L	L	E	J	A
M	S	F	M	T	R	I	H	I	L
P	S	D	S	W	Z	B	E	J	N
Z	R	Z	R	W	U	B	G	Y	F
R	A	Q	V	A	X	G	D	D	M
O	U	Z	C	K	P	A	Y	D	Q
M	G	W	M	A	A	O	A	L	U
P	A	Y	J	P	W	G	E	S	Y
U	J	H	I	S	I	J	Z	L	B
O	Q	H	A	I	H	L	R	Z	C

Word Search 14

R	F	Y	Q	F	Z	K	G	Z	M
K	A	Z	O	M	Y	J	M	P	O
R	N	Z	F	I	S	E	P	E	O
D	V	R	K	P	E	J	K	S	S
D	P	D	Y	R	J	T	D	C	E
E	J	W	K	G	X	R	B	L	L
V	I	A	T	Q	A	A	Y	J	P
D	T	N	Z	Z	W	N	D	K	F
S	J	A	I	F	X	H	D	K	Y
P	F	L	G	R	O	I	A	G	J

Word Search 15

Y	F	O	L	K	X	O	K	O	S
H	M	Z	G	G	X	S	C	F	T
Q	S	A	V	T	M	T	Z	C	V
X	V	S	N	O	O	R	P	Y	Q
F	X	X	M	P	S	I	A	L	I
E	K	M	U	H	K	C	R	V	J
Z	M	S	F	E	B	H	R	X	D
O	E	Z	V	C	J	E	O	V	K
S	R	Y	I	F	X	S	T	Z	S
O	F	A	K	H	R	V	S	C	L

Word Search 16

O	M	N	G	J	F	W	S	D	K
G	Y	I	V	U	T	S	R	F	R
P	C	H	J	T	G	M	A	P	J
P	O	Z	M	E	U	R	E	J	V
Z	O	N	X	O	K	L	B	F	V
X	V	N	I	B	I	T	R	Q	G
H	X	P	I	C	F	R	A	E	I
R	L	S	A	E	T	Q	L	S	S
J	Y	N	N	S	S	E	O	E	W
L	S	K	D	X	B	V	P	L	P

Word Search 17

S	C	O	R	P	I	O	N	S	T
I	J	S	Q	X	V	P	E	T	L
X	X	L	R	W	K	S	K	R	K
L	H	O	V	E	R	Z	B	O	L
Y	O	Q	X	O	T	S	Y	Q	V
E	M	H	H	J	U	S	Z	M	T
J	Q	A	T	U	B	C	O	I	C
G	E	A	H	Q	D	N	J	O	E
S	O	C	A	Y	H	V	S	T	R
K	Y	G	O	I	D	X	Z	L	P

Word Search 18

J	J	S	G	U	T	T	H	F	W
S	P	E	O	N	R	D	T	S	H
S	M	L	Z	Q	P	I	P	A	S
D	Z	T	U	Y	P	I	D	X	I
W	D	R	A	R	X	W	T	A	F
Z	V	U	I	N	D	Z	N	P	R
M	X	T	C	A	V	Y	U	R	A
X	W	Q	S	W	A	N	S	I	T
V	Z	B	H	P	S	G	X	L	S
X	X	X	C	W	U	K	G	C	K

Word Search 19

P	Z	Y	X	A	X	D	H	X	V
F	H	A	N	T	E	A	T	E	R
M	D	Z	T	L	U	C	B	C	S
A	R	M	A	D	I	L	L	O	E
A	D	D	E	H	D	D	Y	S	L
B	V	K	E	T	U	Q	D	E	A
U	Y	U	Q	X	H	R	D	V	H
N	G	Q	X	H	I	H	G	L	W
Q	G	W	V	I	Q	M	T	O	K
Q	D	Z	C	I	G	Z	D	W	M

Word Search 20

P	V	I	C	C	W	E	R	T	S
J	C	H	I	P	M	U	N	K	S
S	J	O	L	A	F	F	U	B	Z
S	N	B	E	H	A	O	J	S	N
U	E	E	P	H	J	H	V	A	R
W	E	F	K	A	S	E	B	E	B
K	N	Y	J	C	C	O	W	S	G
P	P	D	O	C	I	S	E	O	A
E	X	H	A	Y	W	H	L	S	G
N	W	J	R	P	H	P	C	Q	V

Word Search 21

O	U	I	A	U	Y	D	R	V	A
B	Q	P	M	C	B	V	I	V	A
X	L	E	A	N	D	I	H	C	E
O	I	K	D	V	K	K	P	Z	D
V	S	R	T	V	X	V	N	R	S
D	O	N	K	E	Y	S	K	F	J
T	D	M	E	U	G	F	J	V	Q
L	C	E	A	K	J	W	S	A	F
Z	M	H	E	J	M	Q	W	M	F
G	I	P	J	R	M	K	I	Q	M

Word Search 22

X	E	B	Q	S	X	O	D	P	S
H	G	O	A	T	S	U	R	G	X
S	B	L	N	A	W	X	I	S	U
R	F	M	V	I	T	P	G	D	O
L	H	J	C	W	A	Q	C	I	I
L	O	S	T	E	R	R	E	F	C
A	D	A	N	S	Y	V	H	C	J
M	B	I	K	P	C	V	Q	K	H
A	U	K	Z	N	X	S	H	E	W
G	S	F	B	L	Q	J	C	E	Y

Word Search 23

I	**P**	**L**	**A**	**T**	**Y**	**P**	**U**	**S**	P
S	Q	F	H	S	K	Z	A	**S**	T
H	M	R	Y	A	L	H	V	**N**	V
S	J	U	A	C	V	D	W	**O**	W
S	**E**	**N**	**I**	**P**	**U**	**C**	**R**	**O**	**P**
S	V	N	B	S	K	G	Y	**C**	D
U	M	N	P	L	H	L	I	**C**	G
W	D	L	C	Q	X	J	R	**A**	N
C	G	N	M	N	D	W	N	**R**	I
E	N	U	P	H	Q	R	Y	I	S

Word Search 24

Y	W	A	X	M	L	T	Z	I	R
E	N	R	L	T	T	Z	T	N	X
X	D	B	E	E	P	T	D	H	O
Y	S	R	S	E	U	N	P	P	D
D	L	K	E	H	D	A	K	G	V
N	H	H	U	H	A	N	F	D	C
M	S	I	D	N	K	R	I	C	V
X	L	Y	C	X	K	P	K	E	B
N	Q	U	W	N	D	S	Q	S	R
Y	M	C	T	G	M	G	D	E	R

Word Search 25

C	L	V	M	B	B	O	I	P	F
K	V	M	C	N	A	L	O	P	S
M	S	S	L	V	V	F	U	Q	S
R	M	K	J	F	Y	B	U	H	T
Y	M	R	B	I	X	I	T	L	I
V	V	O	A	X	R	O	X	X	I
V	S	T	O	R	L	Z	L	W	N
M	N	S	E	S	K	W	V	Z	F
R	A	L	O	B	J	N	Q	K	E
M	S	K	K	N	J	H	R	E	G

Word Search 26

U	W	I	K	C	O	S	E	S	J
I	V	W	J	Z	L	T	S	F	M
Z	M	N	A	A	G	U	O	P	M
T	B	J	M	D	R	R	Z	V	O
U	A	M	E	L	Q	K	K	D	S
X	A	F	A	L	B	E	I	K	T
M	F	W	N	F	A	Y	A	H	X
L	V	T	Y	D	X	Y	G	H	X
F	F	E	M	F	S	M	S	J	A
Z	I	J	Y	A	C	I	N	O	U

Word Search 27

T	A	B	G	U	V	S	F	R	I
T	N	N	N	M	I	K	O	N	J
N	C	A	T	T	L	E	Q	W	X
J	M	X	F	E	A	S	G	B	M
U	Y	O	C	D	L	C	Q	L	N
H	K	O	D	P	D	O	R	Y	L
U	B	B	L	D	K	M	P	P	U
S	S	E	T	O	Y	O	C	E	E
S	K	R	A	V	D	R	A	A	S
E	V	N	T	K	D	S	Q	I	M

Word Search 28

X	P	G	L	X	A	H	W	P	G
K	A	O	Q	E	Y	Z	R	S	O
A	N	Z	G	Y	M	M	M	G	R
A	T	U	W	I	M	U	M	F	I
C	H	V	T	C	S	Z	R	R	L
R	E	E	K	S	F	S	S	S	L
W	R	M	O	B	V	M	D	V	A
G	S	P	M	I	O	K	V	Q	S
S	O	H	A	W	G	I	O	P	R
Q	I	Z	P	F	X	H	E	T	C

Word Search 29

Y	V	A	V	W	G	B	J	D	W
T	Z	K	O	B	O	J	C	F	P
G	W	N	V	U	Y	U	W	U	W
V	R	F	I	O	N	Z	F	M	E
D	C	I	B	F	X	F	P	L	A
M	W	Q	X	W	I	N	X	F	S
Z	X	X	E	N	R	Z	D	W	E
C	O	O	S	Q	Q	B	G	T	L
S	E	S	I	O	T	R	O	T	S
H	C	U	V	I	N	S	D	E	E

Word Search 30

M	P	L	**A**	F	X	H	E	H	D
S	F	Y	**M**	E	X	W	B	U	M
E	M	H	**P**	W	C	S	V	F	P
N	K	M	**H**	F	Z	A	R	L	P
U	J	C	**I**	O	S	L	A	H	Q
T	M	Q	**B**	R	J	Q	F	F	E
I	H	E	**I**	B	B	X	V	I	P
X	A	E	**A**	F	Q	L	Q	E	Q
I	F	A	**N**	F	T	T	N	Y	F
A	Z	H	**S**	J	O	S	U	Y	D

Made in the USA
Monee, IL
12 April 2023

d7185765-f365-44d6-a278-907aa020ff31R01